TO BE A DOCTOR

—————————————

THE YOUNG PRINCES

—————————————

THE RACE AND THE RUNNER

A Partial List of Books
by Félix Martí-Ibáñez, M.D.

To Be A Doctor

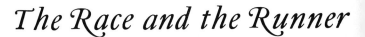

The Young Princes

The Race and the Runner

by FELIX MARTI-IBAÑEZ, M.D.

Editor-in-Chief of the Medical Newsmagazines
MD, MD of Canada, MD en Español, and MD Pacific;
Former Professor and Chairman of the Department
of the History of Medicine, New York Medical College.

MD PUBLICATIONS, INC. *New York*

*To the medical students of today,
the physicians of tomorrow,
who with their dedication and their deeds
will create the medical history
of the future.*

CONTENTS

TO BE
A
DOCTOR

To Be A Doctor

M Y COURSE on the history of medicine had ended. Facing me were a hundred and twenty-eight young men and women. There were pale faces and swarthy faces, students with dark, blond, or red hair, but throughout the entire group the same restless light shone in their young eyes, as if they had captured a spark from the sun. These freshmen of mine asked me to tell them what it means "to be a doctor," and I ended my course with this explanation:

Ever since the day you first said those magic words, "I want to be a doctor," you have been wrapped in the colorful fabric of the history of medicine, a fabric woven from the ideals, wisdom, endeavors, and achievements of our glorious predecessors in medicine.

You have just embarked on a fascinating

voyage leading to the harbor of one of the most dynamic professions. Year after year new windows will keep opening before your eyes, revealing the multifaceted landscape of medical art and science.

But medicine today is so complex that no human mind can possibly absorb it all, as was possible a few centuries ago. Only by using the history of medicine as a gigantic frame to contain what you learn is it possible to integrate the numerous fragments of medical theory and practice that will be taught you in your student years. Only through the history of medicine can one appreciate that to be a doctor, in the true sense of the word, is to be not only a wise man but, above all, a good man. To be a doctor is, in other words, to be a whole man, who fulfills his task as a scientist with professional quality and integrity; as a human being, with a kind heart and high ideals; and as a member of society, with honesty and efficiency.

Contemporary medicine is founded on a series of events that resulted from the thoughts and deeds of a few men in the course of history. History is made by men, and the greatest among the makers of history is the physician because of the effects of his ministry on all other human beings.

Man is the only creature able to make tools with which to make other tools, and of all the tools made by him words are the most important. The fabric of medicine is woven with words that express the ideas from which they sprang. The original meaning of the three words—physician, medic, doctor—that describe our profession is highly illuminating. The word "physician" derives from the Greek *physis*, or nature, denoting that the physician has his roots in an understanding of the nature of things; the word "medic" comes from *mederi*, to heal, and the root *med* means to meditate or think, so that medic is equivalent to thinker and healer; the word "doctor" originally meant master, instructor. Thus, semantically, our profession involves learning, knowing, healing, and teaching.

In its turn, the word "medicine" not only means what medical men do (many of the great figures in medical history, such as Pasteur and Leeuwenhoek, were not physicians), but also denotes a *social* science that uses the methods of the natural sciences to attain four objectives: to promote health, to restore health, to prevent disease, and to rehabilitate the patient.

Every day, more and more, medicine becomes, above all, the prevention of disease and the promotion of health. For only by knowing the healthy man can we cure him when he falls ill. Knowledge of the healthy man is obtained by studying our fellow beings, both the healthy and the diseased, not only in the mirror of classical and modern medical literature but also in current newspapers. You will then learn that poverty is still the main social cause of disease, just as it was in archaic times.

The history of medicine epitomizes the history of civilization. The history of man has passed through three great stages: man learned to master nature by yielding to her laws; he learned to live in society by establishing the first communities; he acquired consciousness of his human dignity and of his ability to forge his own destiny, which in turn enabled him to acquire greatness.

The physician in his threefold capacity, as a

professional, as a member of society, and as a human being, has throughout history helped man in his physical, mental, and social ascent. As a professional man in particular, the physician has always acted as a healer, using magic, faith, empiricism, or rational resources; as a knower, for he knows the secrets of nature and of the human being; as a preventer, for he can arrest disease by forestalling its vanguards before they arrive; and as an organizer, for he can guide society in fighting the historicosocial process called disease. To heal, to know, to prevent, to organize—these will be your four future spheres of professional activity, embraced in the expression "to be a doctor."

To be a doctor, then, means much more than to dispense pills or to patch up or repair torn flesh and shattered minds. To be a doctor is to be an intermediary between man and God.

You have chosen the most fascinating and dynamic profession there is, a profession with the highest potential for greatness, since the physician's daily work is wrapped up in the subtle web of history. Your labors are linked with those of your colleagues who preceded you in history and those who are now working all over the world. It is this spiritual unity with our colleagues of all periods and of all countries that has made medicine so universal and eternal. For this reason we must study and try to imitate the lives of the great doctors of history. Their lives, blazing with greatness, teach us that our profession is the only one that still speaks of its duties in this world of today, in which almost everyone else speaks only of his rights.

An ideal of service permeates all our activities: service especially to the patient, as a fellow creature isolated on the island of his suffering, whom only you can restore to the mainland of health. For that purpose you must know thoroughly not only the diseased but also the healthy.

Your own contributions to medicine can begin even in the golden years of student life. There is no need to wait for your medical degree to start making medical history. Many physicians while still students made historic contributions to medical science: Vesalius, Stensen, Laennec, Remak, Freud, Best, men who believed in themselves and were dedicated to the profession you have chosen for your own.

From now on your professional conduct must adhere to the moral code of medicine that began with the Hippocratic oath. Despite its negative aspect in prohibiting a number of activities, the Hippocratic oath was not a law but a precept self-imposed by physicians who accepted an ideal of devotion and service conjoined by their moral conscience. Five types of ethical duties must guide your life: duties to your teachers, to society, to your patients, to your colleagues, and to yourselves.

You have duties to your teachers, because they, the parents of your mind, are the most important people in your life next to your own parents. I do not mean only your university professors, but any physician from whom you learn anything—his science, art, ethics, self-denial, or example—that may become a source of inspiration in your professional life. You must honor your masters with devotion and friendship, for friendship is man's noblest sentiment, greater even than love.

Your duty to society is to be idealists, not

hedonists: as physicians, to accept your profession as a service to mankind, not as a source of profit; as investigators, to seek the knowledge that will benefit your fellow beings; as clinicians, to alleviate pain and heal the sick; as teachers, to share and spread your knowledge and always because you are imbued with an ideal of service and not the ambition for gain. Thus will you maintain the dignity of our profession as a social science applied to the welfare of mankind.

Your duty to your patients will be to act toward them as you would wish them to act toward you: with kindness, with courtesy, with honesty. You must learn when and how to withhold the truth from your patients if by not telling them all the facts of the case you can relieve or console them, for you can cure them sometimes, and you can give them relief often, but hope you can give them *always*. Remember that a laboratory report is not an irrevocable sentence. A hematological determination, a roentgenogram, an electroencephalogram may supply vital information on the organic working of the body, but it is even more vital never to forget that, behind all such reports and data, there is a human being in pain and anguish, to whom you must offer something more than an antibiotic, an injection, or a surgical aid; you must, with your attitude, your words, and your actions, inspire confidence and faith and give understanding and consolation.

To your colleagues you have the obligations of civilized men sharing a great and noble task and fighting for a common cause in a great crusade. Medicine lives and is nourished by the great social prestige it enjoys. Thus, never speak ill of a colleague, since to do so would be the same as speaking evil of medicine and therefore of your own selves. If you have something good to say about a fellow physician, say it everywhere; if you have not, then keep silent. You belong to a team of gallant professionals of all races and eras, bound together across the ages and continents by a glorious ideal.

Finally, you will have obligations to yourselves. Every man in his youth forms an ideal profile of himself or of what he wants to be. He envisions, while young, an ideal program of things to do in life. The rest of his life is spent trying to fill in that profile with achievements. Some fail to reach fulfillment, and later it is tragic to see that ideal profile, of which they dreamed during their youth, in ruins, with the stumps of things begun but never completed. But in the majority of cases, that ideal silhouette created in youthful days really represents our true selves. You must live to be worthy of that silhouette. Your life, your work, and your personality as a physician must be such that your ideal profile of yourself will be filled in with brilliant achievements.

Learn to live perceptively, using that key to wisdom that comes from seeing everything with a total perspective and in view of eternity. Learn through science to correlate things in space, through history, to correlate events in time, and combine all this knowledge aesthetically through the beauty of art.

You are embarking on a noble career in which there is no room for amateurs or dilettanti, a career in which we must all aspire to be masters of whatever we undertake, for the mistakes of medical carpenters and prescribers' apprentices can have tragic results.

Remember that the important thing in life is to be great, not big, a *great* man, not a big man. Let your actions be great, but preserve your personal modesty and humility. What counts in a man and in a physician is his greatness. By greatness I mean grandeur in the things we do and simplicity in the way we do them, doing things that influence the lives of many people, but preserving always the greatest personal simplicity. For greatness *is* simplicity. Know how to feel yourself an important part of the deeds of history. Try to find out as soon as you can what your ideal self is. Try to be what you truly are; otherwise you will be nothing. Such was Pindar's theme: "Be what thou art." Man's dignity rests in his ability to choose his destiny. You have chosen the best destiny of all, a life of dedicated service and dynamic activity. If you work with faith and without dismay, all your dreams will come true.

In your future work you will be in good company. The great physicians of history, the glorious figures of the past, will always be near you. When you perform a dissection, a red-bearded young man with flashing eyes, Andreas Vesalius, will be peering over your shoulder; when you make a physiological experiment, the melancholy, pensive eyes of William Harvey will be watching you; when you teach medicine, the venerable figure of William Osler with his Apollonian head will come and sit like a medical Goethe beside you; and when you approach the sickbed, the shades of Hippocrates, Sydenham, and Fleming will gather round to counsel you.

The Greeks created the legend that Delphi, site of the famous oracle, was the center of the world, because if two eagles were to fly from any two points of the globe, sooner or later they would meet in Delphi. We now know that the two eagles of science and medicine do not fly only in space but also in time, and their wings hover over the illustrious shadows of the investigators, clinicians, educators, pioneers, rebels, and martyrs of the history of medicine. The meeting place of those two eagles lies not in space but in time, in the future, and in the mind and the heart of every one of you who answered destiny's call to greatness when you decided "to be a doctor."

THE
YOUNG
PRINCES

The Young Princes

ABOUT SEVEN thousand medical students—
the young princes in the kingdom of medicine—will graduate this year from American
colleges. With this annual explosion of youth,
the rosebush of medicine will blossom afresh
in full brilliance and fragrance. This is a good
moment to consider the role of the student in
the history of medicine and the role of the
history of medicine in the student's education.

If there are two figures in medicine whose
social status has changed in the course of the
centuries, they are the surgeon and the student. In the case of the student, the social
antagonism he aroused in the past had its
source in the revenge he took against the
rigors of student life. In the Middle Ages,
poor students whose families were unable to
support them often had to beg on street cor-

ners. Fortunately in those days, as in many Eastern countries even today, begging was not a shameful act but a devotional one.

Many students lived in gloomy cubbyholes, with naked, mildewed walls, small paneless windows, and straw-covered floors. Always cold and hungry, these poor students fed every morning on the hope of getting, by fair means or foul, a piece of sausage or boiled tripe. They drank warm beer, often in the company of their teachers on the eve of examinations, which both parties attended the next day with a royal hangover! They reveled in street brawling and were the terror of the towns they lived in, so much so that as night fell, the townspeople would lock up their houses, trembling for the survival of their old wines and the virtue of their young daughters.

Classes began at five in the morning, and the students, who had risen at four, numb with cold and without breakfast, had to stand for hours or sit on the freezing hard floor during lectures, which sometimes lasted fourteen hours a day with only a short break for lunch. Afterward, back in their dismal cold rooms, they would study for hours on end by the flickering light of a candle. Even so, the thirst for knowledge was so strong that students flocked in thousands to the universities and stood for hours in the public squares of Paris or Padua, Bologna or Oxford to listen to the learned discourses of Albertus Magnus, Pietro d'Abano, Taddeo Alderotti, Arnold of Villanova, or other eminent teachers of the age.

Much time passed before the medical profession gained—in the eighteenth century—social status, crowned with respect and privilege, and the medical student won the consideration and comfort that his studies merited. In any event, the "official" irruption of the medical student into the history of medicine came comparatively late. Although, as Galen relates, medical students in imperial Rome were often mere children, sons of physicians, who practiced dissection under the watchful eye of their fathers, and in medieval times also they began their studies at an early age, the medical student, from the mere nature of his occupation, was considered a man in miniature rather than a child.

Students practiced a thousand wiles at

every turn in their fight against hunger, employing bold and ingenious artifices. One need only read the masterpieces of the Spanish picaresque novelists to learn some of the stratagems to which hunger pushed them. The great seventeenth-century satirist Francisco de Quevedo tells of the trick played by a famished student who passed a yard where a woman was feeding her plump chickens handfuls of corn. The unwary woman kept crying, "*pío, pío*," the word used in Spanish-speaking countries to call chickens, just as we use "kitty" to call a cat. The student, with a perfectly straight face, promptly informed the startled woman that to use a pope's name (Pius, in Spanish, *Pío*) for calling chickens was a sacrilege, which the Inquisition would punish at the stake, and that the chickens thus called were condemned as profane. Whereupon, with the consent of the terrified woman, the wily student carried off under his cloak the "excommunicated" chickens, which, after they were deliciously roasted, wound up in his own hungry belly and in those of his equally ravenous fellow students.

Despite their workaday problems, many

students have made important contributions to medicine during their college years. Among other things, this proves that scientific discovery does not wait on age and may be achieved as well by the adolescent as by the aged and that the student need only know how to "invent his own duties," beyond those imposed by his curriculum, for him to make history.

In his admirable book, aptly entitled *Young Endeavour,* Professor William Gibson describes the great medical discoveries and contributions made by students during the past four centuries. The list is impressive and enlightening. A few examples are: Vesalius' pregraduation discoveries in anatomy; Lorenzo Bellini's discovery as a student of the renal tubules in a stag; Henry Gray's study of the comparative anatomy of the optic nerves while at St. George's Hospital Medical School in London; Joseph Lister's student papers on the contractile tissue of the iris; Ramón y Cajal's studies in his youth on bones, which incidentally were stolen from cemeteries; the two thousand thumbnail biographies written by Albrecht von Haller at the age of eight and the

Greek dictionary with Chaldean and Hebrew
equivalents he prepared when ten years old;
John Shaw Billings' modern concept of a medical reference library born while he was per-
forming "that melancholy duty," preparing
his graduation thesis; William Harvey's obser-
vations on chicken embryos, made with his
master Fabricius ab Aquapendente in Padua;
Ehrlich's pregraduation paper published in
Archives of Microscopic Anatomy outlining
his theory of histological affinity for certain
dyes; Niels Stensen's discovery as a student of
the parotid duct bearing his name; Claude
Bernard's studies of gastric juice; Ivan Pav-
lov's studies on the pancreatic fistula; Paul
Langerhans' studies on microscopic anatomy
of the pancreas; Pierre Marie's discovery of
the sign of tremor in the hand and digits in
thyroid diseases; William Osler's first paper on
the microscopy of some algae he found in a
barrel one Christmas Eve; the self-immolation
of the Peruvian student Daniel Carrión when
he inoculated himself with blood from a
patient with verruga peruana and proved it to
be a form of Oroya fever; Sigmund Freud's
studies on the nervous system of a lower in-

vertebrate; Jean Pecquet's discovery of the thoracic duct; Max von Pettenkofer's identification of arsenic with a Marsh apparatus; and the discovery of insulin by Charles H. Best with Frederick Banting; and many others. Numerous indeed are the discoveries made by medical students.

Having shown the two sides of the medal, the glory and the misery of the medical student in history, let us now consider what the student should have the right to demand in his medical education.

Every student of medicine has the right to learn his profession as a response to the innermost call of his vocation. In this process he will acquire a means of earning a living, and also a greater knowledge of man and the universe and a means of developing his personality as a human being. Medical education undertakes to provide him with a vast amount of knowledge that will help him develop his profession with ability. Unfortunately, such knowledge often makes of him a specialist instead of a physician, a technician instead of a scientist, an expert instead of a man. And I believe that *the student* should influence his teachers, even as they influence him, by demanding what will be most useful to him in his future professional life.

Obviously the concept of what will be "most useful" to him is a relative one. I would say the most important thing is that both the student and the teacher recognize that it is more important to be a *professional*, that is to say, a man endowed with a general knowledge of his profession and a specialized knowledge of its techniques, than to be a mere medical technologist or artisan. Originally only theology, medicine, and law were recognized as "professions," that is to say, the three branches of human knowledge that since prehistoric times have tried to minister to inexplicable moral afflictions, physical diseases, and lawsuits and disputes. Of these three professions, medicine down the ages has kept its singleness of purpose unchanged in the hands of physicians—those men endowed, according to Homer, with "knowledge beyond that of all other men."

As the centuries have passed, a stricter criterion has been established in the selection of students of medicine, and the relationship between student and teacher has become increasingly closer. Not yet, however, has a philosophy of medical education been established on the basis that the important thing is .not just to instruct the student but to *educate* him, that medical instruction, based on the study of its technology, must be replaced by medical *education*. In other words, knowledge of the philosophy and history of medicine must precede knowledge of its technology.

Indeed, the brave Kentucky physician, Daniel Drake, of whom William Osler said, "In many ways he [is] the most unique figure in the history of American Medicine . . ." himself asserted that "literature and science are not the same; but a physician should acquire both, and the cultivation of the former should precede that of the latter." And in our own time, a voice that can hardly be accused of cultural dilettantism, that of the eminent chemist Conant, has said, "In terms of general education, poetry and philosophy are of vastly more importance than science." To that I would add the study of the history, art, philosophy, and literature of all peoples as a means of knowing mankind better. Litera-

ture, like poetry, reflects man's dreams,
thoughts, and visions, but history records the
deeds and actions of mankind as a whole.
"History is a clinical study of man in society,"
as Sir Richard Livingstone said. And since
medicine is merging more and more each day
with medical anthropology—the study of the
image of man in health and disease considered
in both space and time, that is, in his country and society and in his passage through
historical time—medical anthropology should
also be added to the student's basic education.

Yet today too many specialists and tech-
nologists without any basic scientific preparation are being created. This might eventually
turn medicine from a profession into a technology and degrade the noble medical education into a mere vocational training. But that
is not so important as the molding of *men*,
men who later, if they so wish, can become
specialists. For in our profession the general
practitioner preceded the specialist for many
centuries.

Nothing is better than the history of medicine for instilling into the medical student a
high sense of his professional mission, history

taught not for the purpose of making the student an historian on a small scale, but of making him a better physician by making him a better man. For the history of medicine is medicine, but above all it is history. In other words, it is a study of man in society, of his supreme greatness and his tragic errors, and it teaches the concatenation of ideas through the ages, the living panorama of the human mind in full creativity, the relative value of truth and error in science, the relativity of human knowledge, the duty of "equanimity."

Taught not as a musty recital of names and dates but as a living tapestry of human figures brought back to life by the magic of the teacher's and the student's enthusiasm, the history of medicine creates an historical conscience in the student within which he can frame the scattered, fragmentary learning acquired in the classroom.

Of course, when the student takes his medical degree, it will matter little whether he knows the date when Vesalius' *Fabrica* was published or when Harvey announced his famous discovery, but the accumulated cen-

turies-long experience of his predecessors will
be a priceless spiritual guide for his thoughts
and for his hands in the practice of his profession. It will give him moral fortitude, wisdom, understanding, and tolerance toward
his patients, his colleagues, and his teachers,
toward himself and toward society. With the
history of medicine, that loom of rich individual experiences on which the multicolored
fabric of the past is woven, the student can
clothe the shivering nudity of his technologi-
cal accomplishments and give them warmth
and color.

What, therefore, must the university teach
students?

From my teacher, Dr. Gregorio Marañón,
I learned that the university must create in the
student that "university spirit" that seeks the
truth rather than scientific erudition, shows
tolerance, cultivates scientific curiosity, re-
spects investigation techniques, and is eager
"to invent duties" beyond those imposed by
the curriculum. Only then will the student re-
spond to his vocation—that inner voice that
calls us to a particular profession—through
love of duty and efficiency in doing. The uni-

versity must also teach the student not just to be a sportsman obsessed by the "chase for high marks," which, after all, are not of much value in professional life, but to create new tasks for himself, to be guided by sincere inclinations rather than by mere aptitude. The teacher's mission is to diagnose inclinations rather than to determine aptitudes. In doing so, he may discover a future medical genius, who sometimes happens to be a mediocre student, perhaps because his genius already makes him rebel against standard academic teaching.

The teacher must encourage the student's own originality and imagination, setting himself as the example to be followed by continuing to be himself a student who is always learning and not a dogmatic teacher.

No great teacher has ever liked to repeat his courses word by word, preferring instead to create something original each year, stimulated by the young minds in his care. Hence all great teachers, remembering the agonies of their student years, have always opposed the present educational system, which, particularly in Europe, is often barbarously medieval in its demands on the student. I myself, educated in Europe and having graduated in medicine in Europe on the highest academic plane, say yet that the high marks I got and the university honors conferred on me left me with only the desire to campaign for a change in that system of medical education for the benefit of the student.

This too is why I believe that every teacher achieves his best educational work not from his professional chair, however eminent he may be, but through his free and independent work, that work accomplished in the chair of everyday life, where the teacher through his words, his pen, his thoughts, and, above all, his example exerts his influence not only on students and colleagues, but also on those who read his writings or enjoy from afar the intellectual fruits of his labor.

All this means that the history of medicine interpreted as a living and dynamic history of dreams, enthusiasms, efforts and achievements, failures and miseries, and as a passionate chronicle of the eternal quest for medical truth, must be the compass to guide student life from its beginning. I also believe that this history must be interpretative, not just descriptive; that is, it must correlate facts and ideas, the past and the present, as a means of anticipating the future. It must also be a romantic epic and a quixotic and idealistic crusade.

The student in our profession becomes more important every day as a catalyst for the school of medicine as well as a future man of medicine. In this day and age, when everyone flaunts his rights, the student has the opportunity to dedicate himself solely to his *duties* —those imposed by the university and those he himself invents—that is to say, the duties to be a whole man, a good citizen, an expert in his profession, and, above all, to be faithful to those tasks that stimulate in him the vision of history as a spur to his own dreams. If he understands his mission this way, the student —that young prince of our profession—may hold in his hands the power to become the strongest and brightest thread in the fabric of medicine.

THE RACE
AND
THE RUNNER

The Race
and the Runner

Of all the sports I pursued—with more
enthusiasm than skill—during what is euphe-
mistically called "extreme youth," none, not
even soccer or handball or swimming, of
which I was, and still am, extremely fond,
gave me as much pleasure as foot racing. Running—and I became a very fast runner—
fascinated me, possibly because I uncon-
sciously felt the exciting conflict that all racing
truly entails: to cover the greatest possible
space in the least possible time.

As an adult, racing has continued to fasci-
nate me, but since my legs no longer care to
run any faster than is necessary to catch a bus,
I now do all my racing through my travels and
my work. The swift electronic eagle of the jet
has allowed me to race around the whole

globe, just as the typewriter, pounded at such speed as only two fingers allow, has facilitated my work in that fascinating race of filling paper with symbols like the tracks of a small bird on wet sand. Perhaps that youthful fondness for foot racing has moved me to meditate on the meaning of man's other race, his professional career. It is highly significant that in Spanish the word *carrera* means both career and racing!

THE RACE AND THE ARCHER

At the beginning of his *Nicomachean Ethics*, Aristotle said: "Shall we not, like archers who have a mark to aim at, be more likely to hit upon what is right?" The symbol of the archer has figured prominently in the history of philosophy. The archer with his arrows—whether they are made of bamboo or crystal, whether they score a bull's-eye or plunge to the ground halfway along their course like a burned-out rocket—is also a symbol of life, of what we want to do. But, contrary to what so many philosophers once thought, life is not a passive "being," that is, something cut and dried, not permanent substance in nature, but rather it is doing things over a period of time. Life is more than static nature; it is history and biography. As Fichte said, "Our philosophy becomes the history of our own heart and life." For him, true reality was *Tätigkeit*: activity, dynamism, exploit. Confronting the things of his world, man asserts himself through pure activity, through constantly "making" himself.

THE "DOING" OF MAN

In nature, the star and the shrub, the frog and the rock, the river and the nightingale, all these things exist, that is, they merely have a being. They are what they are because they can be nothing else. Man is the only creature who makes his own life. He becomes what he is through a continuous doing, which entails constant choosing among the many things he can do and constant toiling to do them. This faculty of deciding what he wants to do or what he can do is both man's glory and his tragedy. For, as the Hindu proverb says, "Each step we take can be the beginning of a hundred different paths."

Therefore what man does is a race, a ca-

reer, and man's career, whether that of a physician, explorer, engineer, or television direc-
tor, is the root and core of his life, since the
business of being a man rests first and foremost on *doing something*. Work is a sexual
characteristic of the male. The Venetian ad-
venturer Casanova did nothing in life except
seduce credulous masked damsels in the frol-
icsome Venice of the Age of Enlightenment
and stake purses of gold pieces on the drop of
a card. Paradoxically, for that reason, despite
his vast and varied menu of seduced women at
the erotic marathon banquet that was his life,
Casanova was not a true man. By shirking all
real work, he forfeited the main psychosexual
characteristic of a real man.

The real man, whether in San Francisco or
Singapore, in Bogotá or Nairobi, runs in life,
makes a career, a race (I include in this concept not only the professions but all technical
and manual skills), doing so not on a cinder
track like that of a stadium, but with brow or
hand in the vast arena of life.

A career ought to be—unfortunately it is
not always so, even in medicine—synonymous
with vocation. "To career" means to run from

one place to another, following a set path which we ourselves choose or invent. In the age of the Caesars, the term "career" was applied to races in an arena between quadrigae drawn by slavering horses that, goaded by the rider's whip, tore around the arena enveloped in clouds of dust and the thundering clamor of the plebs. Later on, career and race became synonymous with human life. Life was depicted as an arduous race in the stadium of time and space, as a constant effort from beginning to end, as an exhausting chain of toil. Some human beings could complete it successfully; others collapsed like horses felled by a titanic effort.

Life therefore is not just being or standing still or lying down; it is moving along the road. "Life is a race," said Dilthey, ". . . that begins in time and ends in it." Unfortunately, that road is nearly always chosen in youth when we hardly know which road we want to follow. Thus, careers chosen in early youth, like premature marriages, are lottery tickets, the results of which are not known until much, much later.

The irrational beings and the things that

inhabit the universe—the glowworm, the morning star, the starfish, the piece of quartz, the pink geranium—have an already predetermined life; at best, they only succumb to circumstances not of their own doing. (Such circumstances are fascinating in their variety. In the early days of World War II, it is said that Winston Churchill was asked why Great Britain was not acting with greater vigor and efficiency, why she was confining herself purely to defensive measures. The magnificent leader answered that in some waters lobsters require a certain amount of cobalt to develop a defensive shell. While their shells are developing the lobsters protect their soft flesh between rocks. This protective armor of rock is abandoned only when they have developed their own carapace and can live in open waters without fear of being devoured by rapacious fish. Britain, concluded Churchill, was waiting for her defensive carapace to develop before going into action.) But apart from such circumstances—storms, droughts, hunters, wild beasts, fires, floods, earthquakes—beings and things that have no reasoning faculty exist in nature with no other tasks than feeding, protecting, and reproducing themselves.

Man is different. He must choose his life, he must constantly make decisions, and he must begin doing so even before he has any clear notion of what life, his own life, is. Man is the only living creature that has to choose his own future, and he must do so without knowing whether he has made the right choice, just as the *couturiers* in Paris must design their fall collections without knowing whether women will want to wear their creations when the Bois de Boulogne dons its golden mask of dry leaves. Just as women will first explore display windows and showrooms before making their final selection, so should man explore the compartments of his mind before adopting a pattern of life. In doing this he has no better guide than that inner subtle voice called "vocation."

VOCATION AND SERVICE

Webster's dictionary defines "vocation" as "a call; a summons; specific., a calling to a particular state, business, or profession; as, a *vocation* to the religious life." "Career" is de-

fined as "a running, a course, esp. a swift one;
hence, speed," and also, "A profession or
other calling demanding special preparation
and undertaken as a lifework." "Career" derives from the Spanish *carro* meaning wagon,
and the Italian *carriera* and the French
carrière, meaning highroad. The first "career"
was the rapid movement of a wagon. The Oxford English dictionary defines "career" as "A
person's course or progress through life (or a
distinct portion of life). . . . To move at full
speed." And Walter W. Skeat says that
carrière is a racecourse (from late Latin,
carraria via).

In all these definitions, one thing springs to
the eyes, just as a hare unexpectedly jumps
into sight when the huntsman rounds a bend
in the woods: vocation implies an inspiration
or call, a road to be traveled, speed in travel-
ing it, a profession chosen for life. "Career,"
then, is first and foremost a vocation, and a
vocation as genuine as that most genuine of
all vocations—from St. Augustine, the passionate African, and St. Teresa, the gentle
mystic of Castile, to our own times—that of
serving God. The double aspect of career as

vocation and service is what I wish to eluci-
date here.

Vocation, unfortunately, is an inner voice
that usually speaks only in a barely audible
whisper, particularly in our adolescence when
we most need to hear it loud and clear. There
is one way of ascertaining our vocation and
that is to find out what makes us the happiest,
to discover what we like more than anything
else. I have evolved a special "technique" for
finding out whether an adult has a true vocation for his career (too often the person himself does not know). It is a very simple rule
that anyone can use. I call it "the mathematics
of vocation" and it can be summarized in one
sentence: *That occupation—and preoccupation—to which we voluntarily devote most of
the hours of our life is our true vocation.* In
other words, the occupation that makes us
happiest is our true vocation. As for myself
(the person that I know best, of course, though
not thoroughly or perhaps even approxi-
mately), I can say that as far back as I can
remember the occupation that has made me
the happiest and to which I have devoted the
most time during my life is writing.

When Ortega y Gasset, the late magnate of thought, gave his last course on metaphysics at the University of Madrid, he was concerned with man's professional destiny and said many beautiful and profound things. (Unfortunately, they were never published in book form, since death intervened too soon, but the splendid notes taken by Ortega y Gasset's disciples, Manuel Mindán and Agustín Minguijón, were preserved.) Ortega y Gasset reminded his listeners that man must forge his own life by using his imagination, which, according to Goethe, is man's most important faculty. This Goethian assertion seems bold and venturesome. It is not. The scientist may object to such a declaration, but in reality he should be the last to do so, since metaphor is a valuable instrument of science, and, psychologically, scientific thinking is nothing but the fantasy of exactitude, just as metaphor *is* poetry.

Each person has to invent his form and his style: his career. To live authentically, adopting as our guide an imperative of authenticity, we must follow an imperative of invention. Human life is a poetic task: to invent the character we dream of being and should be, to invent the style and the *garbo*, the grace with which we want to embellish our career. In this sense every man has to be the novelist of his own life.

FANTASY AND CHOICE OF CAREER

In choosing a career people fall into two types. One type is not true to his own destiny. This is the man who chooses a career for one of three reasons: routine (all his ancestors were physicians, naturalists, lawyers, or soldiers); money (he is dazzled by the prospects of a Cadillac, a yacht, a country estate, a rich wife, of becoming a fashionable physician on Park Avenue, the Champs Élysées, or Harley Street); or humiliating, spiritless submissiveness to circumstances (forced on him perhaps by relatives or friends who have paid for his education).

The other type of man invents his own career. For that purpose, like a conjurer drawing from his top hat all sorts of things, from multicolored streamers to a white rabbit, he extracts from his fantasy the career that goes with the kind of life that appeals to him.

Although not yet well understood, the influence that the poetic power of our imagination can have on the choice and anticipation of a future life about which we dream is formidable: the planter-to-be envisions a life alternating between tilling his coffee plantation under a sweltering sun and drinking iced beer in his bungalow; the explorer on a Tibetan mountain peak revels in the warmth of the stove in his tent after the wind outside has turned his mustache into stalactites; the scientific investigator relaxes from the long tedious hours of searching for the elusive virus with his electron microscope by playing melodious sonatas on his violin during his leisure hours. In this sense human life is a kind of literature, a pure novel created by our fantasy, and our career is the Nobel prize awarded to that fantasy.

Man in choosing a career has many types of lives to select from, just as an Ottoman sultan of Constantinople had many favorites in his harem from which to choose the one to share the voluptuous blue hours of night alongside the Bosporus. This applies as much to nations as to men. There have been dynamic nations in history, such as Greece, which was grace; Rome, which was command; India, which was reverie (visions can be as dynamic as actions!); and there are nations that have chosen sedentary occupations, such as Switzerland, which is well known for her fondues, precision clocks, and philanthropic societies, to say nothing, as Orson Welles observed, of the cuckoo clock.

When man has a need—our needs, contrary to general belief, are quite limited: food, sleep, love, money—he looks around him for a means of satisfying it. If he does not find what he is seeking, a creative man invents it and satisfies himself in one way or another: his hunger with fruits or plants as in southeast Asia; his sexual desire with mental fantasies or a peculiar form of legerdemain like schoolboys; his sleepiness by dozing in a doorway or even in a standing position, as I saw soldiers do during the Spanish Civil War; his poverty by turning, as poets do, his capital of pennies into millions of dreams.

Man always has a vast treasure within himself. The trouble is that very few people know how to utilize it, and they often search for a

bank to rob when they possess an immeasur-
able fortune within themselves. It has been
said that the poverty-stricken inhabitants of a
certain Central American country with abun-
dant unexploited mines of precious metals are
like "beggars sitting on a bench made of gold
and silver." The same thing could be said of
many people. From the late Spanish play-
wright and Nobel laureate for literature,
Jacinto Benavente, comes this sentence that
we would all do well to remember: "It is a
very sad thing in life when we are asked for
gold and can give only copper; but it is still
sadder when we give gold and are told: 'Copper would have been enough!'"

Perhaps man does not really create patterns
of life as an act of pure creation in his fantasy.
Sometimes he merely fills in professional gaps
in his society, as when death or other reasons
leave a community without dentists or nurses.
In such instances, his career is dictated by the
needs of society, not by a free, personal deci-
sion. At other times, he may merely reproduce
life patterns, and every life pattern is, in a psy-
chological sense, an archetype. At the Inter-
national Congress of Psychiatry in Zurich in

1957, whose main theme on that occasion was schizophrenia, I personally heard Carl Jung—robust and rustic-looking, with a luminous smile—whose medical mind was the most fertile in original ideas in all history, say that human archetypes exist in civilized man just as they did in archaic man and that there is but slight difference between the Bond Street gentleman and the Kenya witch doctor. Each of them selects a form of life from the archetypes carefully stored in the cabinets of his unconscious. In reality, fantasy uses this rich store of unconscious dreams and archetypes as the scenographer uses lights, colors, and backcloths to create his realistic-looking stage effects.

THE DUTY TO LIVE AUTHENTICALLY

There are some men who through an abundance of drive, determination, courage, and imagination have been able to create for themselves a type of life that is authentic because it is original and unprecedented. I have known a few men like that.

Frequently a man chooses a type of life and adopts the career that will lead him to it.

Thus, he may become a physician, an architect, a musician, or a soldier. All these varieties of life have a common denominator, their everyday biological facets. Everyone has to get up, wash, dress, breakfast, work, dine, rest, make love sometimes, and perform other less romantic yet biologically imperative tasks. But each of these lives, like trains, runs along a different track. Although the tracks are different, as are the worlds, the society in which people live may be the same.

The ideal thing is to choose and to live one's own life as something authentic and original, as original as Rembrandt's *Night Watch*, of which only one canvas exists, avoiding the type of life made, so to speak, on an assembly line, like those mass-produced counterfeit Utrillos, with their uniform world of blank walls and narrow streets. The life of an individual should be something nontransferable and distinct from anyone else's, just as love and a career ought to be distinct. Modern society conceives of a career as a road by which each individual races toward his destiny of success or defeat and eventually death, without considering that he may have started down a blind alley that leads nowhere because he has chosen a career without having any vocation for it. Thus, it is essential that we do not confuse two things that have nothing in common, though sometimes by chance they coincide (as sometimes happens with love and marriage), namely, vocation and career.

CAREER AND JOB

Modern semantics has invested the term "career" with an aristocratic significance. In olden times, to be a printer in Basel—like the great Oporinus who produced the *Fabrica*—was to be a "career" man; today it is just a "job." Careers today include those of the diplomat, engineer, attorney, architect, chemist, physician, physicist. Even the writer is not regarded as a career man, in spite of the fact that he is an artist. (The writer is the greatest of all artists, since with only a pencil stub and a scrap of paper he can evoke light, color, sound, scents, pictures, sculpture, music, architecture—a whole world—which makes him the beloved of the gods.)

Now we classify as "career" every activity in which a social framework of intellectuality predominates, and as "job" that activity in which manual skill is dominant. This is wrong, because there are orthopedists whose activity is eminently manual, and there are newspaper reporters whose activity is purely mental. It would be better to speak of "careers of the brow" and "careers of the hand."

The paradox is that too often the manual worker, particularly in large cities, earns more than the brain worker: the plumber more than the researcher, the electrician more than the mathematician. The career often pays less, financially speaking, than the job. It is a sad commentary on our society that certain musical human insects from overseas are paid millions, while some American professors and many a first-class writer have to count the potatoes they eat.

With the advance of technology, the number of careers in our society is continually on the increase. In the days of the stagecoach, when Dick Turpin was the master and terror by night of England's frosted highways, nobody would have thought that postilions would one day be succeeded by chauffeurs in Bentleys and then by astronauts. It has been

said that the Hindu castes were originally
"careers" that had been made hereditary. This
is still the case in France, where vineyard pro-
prietors bring up their sons to be vintners; in
Britain, where merchant shipping houses
dealing with the Far East are handed down
from father to son; and in Switzerland, where
watchmakers train their sons as apprentices to
their own trade.

In ancient times there were not many careers. The clever man knew everything, or
practically everything, there was to know. The
physician was magician, priest, statesman,
and poet all in one. In Egypt, Imhotep cured
patients of ophthalmia, was the Pharaoh's vi-
zier and architect of the Sakkara pyramid in
the Libyan desert. Rome's bridges were
erected by her priests; today a priest probably
could not converse longer than five minutes
with an engineer without having to take ref-
uge in talk about the weather or television.
However, with the exception of a few encyclo-
pedic men, the majority of the people in ancient times were serfs who cleaned the canals
of Mesopotamia, hoisted blocks of stones onto
the Egyptian pyramids, erected Ionic temples,

and soldiered in the phalanxes of Greece, which bristled with spears as a hedgehog bristles with quills.

THE TRANSIENCE OF SCIENCE AND THE ETERNITY OF ART

A career these days, as I have said, requires vocation, liking, creative preoccupation. The medical career in particular requires a vocation of "duty" as well as a vocation of "love," of almost religious devotion to what is to be done, a vocation uninfluenced by false illusions of wealth and glory.

In science, glory does not always crown the name of the man who extracted from the abysmal depths of mystery some knowledge that did not exist before, that is, the man who made the *dis*-covery. We cannot speak of *Don Quixote* without thinking of Cervantes, nor of the *Eroica* without Beethoven, nor of *Moses* without Michelangelo; but hardly anyone remembers the names of the men who developed the tetanus antitoxin and the typhoid vaccine or who invented the hypodermic syringe, the forceps, and the ophthalmoscope. That is why so many scientists resort to an interest outside their profession, to a favorite occupation on the fringes of medicine, impelled by an inner voice that demands that they win a modicum of *personal* immortality. Scientific fame is transient, and because of its swift progress so are the developments of science; artistic fame, on the other hand, is eternal because the evolution of art is slow, sometimes remaining almost motionless in its course. If the physician or the scientist can couple Truth, which is Beauty, with an imperative of disciplined order and clarity in his work and writings, he can make of science an art and of medicine a happy career.

Vocation is often born of the circumstance —time and space, environment—in which one lives. One of the great achievements of J. von Uexküll, a most outstanding biologist of our time, was to demonstrate that all living things live in different worlds, that the world of one entity is not the same as that of another —the world of the jellyfish, the reptile, the philosopher, the sports lover are individual and personal—and that no two creatures have an identical view of the world. Everybody has, then, an extremely individual and personal circumstance, and trying to put this to good purpose, "to reabsorb it," is human destiny, the adventure—or misadventure—of mankind.

Life gains meaning only when we discover our true circumstance, the world and the epoch in which we find ourselves, and, accepting its inexorability, turn it into our own creation. We do not adapt ourselves to it; we adapt it to ourselves. Life is chance, a fateful confrontation with our circumstance; it is a constant struggle to dominate our physical and spiritual environment, in the same way that a good Gaucho masters a wild colt on the sunbathed *pampa*.

Just as a particular fragment of scenery— city, countryside, sea—is multiplied into as many different pictures as there are reflections of it in the mental mirror of each person looking at it, similarly every career is interpreted and exercised by every man in his own style. I would say that the man with the greater chance of success is not he who pursues his career under bondage to duty and obligation, but he who practices it with enthusiasm and imagination, not just out of love for reward, but reveling simply in the splendid adventure of doing what he has to do and doing it magnificently well. That is to say, the man who accepts his living environment and who firmly proceeds to adapt it, to fit it to his individual image, creates through this integration an impassioned, lucid, and finely dramatic life.

Our careers really begin when we stop living in a group, as we all do in our adolescent years, and go forth to face our fates on our own and to fulfill the historic missions that our own generation places in our hands even as in olden times a patriarchal leader handed down his brave sword to his descendant. That moment generally comes at the magic age of twenty-five or twenty-six years, bearing out the concept of the historic generations, of which each generation is composed of fifteen-year periods.

A career is a mere schematic trajectory, an outline, a contour, which we have to fill in with achievement. Vocation is a broad and majestic river bed, an Amazon of the spirit; career is a narrow-gauge railroad. Only the great man can broaden the gauge of his ca-

reer so that the tremendous train of his true
vocation can run on it.

THE MEDICAL CAREER AND SPECIALIZATION

In Medicine, the task of reconciling the
smiling, sunny, and, above all, broad vocation
with one's professional career is becoming increasingly difficult because of the incessant
and rapid increase in scientific knowledge.
This compels the young physician to special-
ize, sometimes before he has completed his
studies. The student begins his studies full of
enthusiasm and expectation; he wants to learn
everything and do everything. Soon he begins
to realize that this is impossible and he is then
compelled to clip the wings of his illusions
with the shears of reality. Thus it is that life
often clips, for young people, the magic, iri-
descent wings of the ideal love, the eternal
friendship, or a glorious career.

When the young physician decides too soon
to become a specialist, he may be curtailing
his personal vocation. Vocation is richer and
much broader than any career, since a career
often leaves outside the orbit of our interests
things that may greatly stimulate our curiosity

and includes other things in which we are not particularly interested. Thus, many dimensions of the activities we have dreamed about remain outside the ambit of our career, and the profiles of our lives then show gaps empty of the desired achievements.

The specialist in any career—however vital, however admirable—is, nevertheless, one of the most tragic figures in modern history, because often he renounces learning a little about almost everything in order to learn almost everything about a little. He prunes the ideal flowers from the garden of his dreams in order to leave room for the wholesome, though often dry, fruits of knowledge. Sometimes he realizes—usually too late—that his chosen pattern of life has become a mere stump, a ruin, a silhouette void of ideal content, however great its scientific content. He learns more each day about one thing and less each day about all the rest. His life becomes impoverished in many areas in order to become enriched in only one. At times specialization is a contradiction to the individual vocation of living and knowing and of being happy.

Of course, there are exceptions. Einstein alternated working on the equations that were to shake the world atomically with violin playing; Fleming alternated exploring the lunar landscape of his molds with his sketching, using bacterial culture broth; Jung and Freud, after plumbing the abysses of the mind, turned to their Egyptian and African collections; Cerletti relaxed from his studies of the electric storms and earthquakes of cerebral seismology by taking care of countless canaries in a beautiful cage (I saw them at his lovely home in Rome) that resounded with golden songs. These are exceptions. But I am an optimistic man. I believe the specialist of the future will learn more and more how to keep his career from restricting his personal project of living, because to live—fully and with dignity, renouncing nothing—is more important than to follow a career. The career of life is more important than the professional career. It is more important to create, that is, to live, than it is to learn.

How can one ascertain what one's true vocation should be and how to develop it into a career that will make one happy and will serve mankind? Is intuition enough? Kant said that thought without intuition is blind but that intuition without a concept is not science.

The main thing, I believe, is to apply to one's vocation and to one's career, that is, to life, a plan of action. Life is a struggle; it is action, it is doing, it is an endeavor that moves forward, always. Man, immutable in his body, his nature essentially unchanged since the time of the Altamira cave paintings, is above all things history and biography, that is, change. That is why he is free, and this freedom is either the scope of his compass or his tragedy.

Everything in man is in motion; it is going on a journey. His personal history, like health and disease, proceeds from something and is proceeding into something. Thus, man must look to the future, though always carrying in his satchel the rich spiritual treasure of the past. He has an imperative for action with regard to things and men, but he must act in accordance with a preconceived plan. His strategic plan is based on a set of *concepts*, the perfect compass for navigating the sea of life. With a clear vocation and a clear concept of what his career should be, he can make a happy and creative life for himself.

During my travels in Japan, I became greatly interested in Zen Buddhism. In Tokyo, in the springtime of 1963, shortly after the wind had swept away the last *sakura*, the cherry blossoms, I had the good fortune to hear an unforgettable address on Zen Buddhism from the lips of Daisetz Suzuki, the venerable, almost centenarian, master. In some spiritual alchemy, perhaps triggered by Zen Buddhism among other things, I have thought out a simple formula that could be a guide in our professional career and a torch to shed light on our race through life: *"Intuition linked to a concept leading to action."*